THE FLOWE

PRICE
STERN
SLOAN

PRICE STERN SLOAN LIMITED, NORTHAMPTON, ENGLAND

It was an especially fine morning
in the land of Do-As-You're-Told.
Tidyup was in his garden.

Tidyup liked his garden. He had grown a particularly large flower and he was rather proud of it.

Suddenly he heard a strange noise.
It was coming from his flower.
He looked closer . . .

And saw Go-to-Bed, fast asleep inside!

Tidyup didn't like that.

He told Go-to-Bed to find
somewhere else to sleep.
Poor Go-to-Bed!

But he wandered off as he'd been asked, and Tidyup carried on with his gardening.

Go-to-Bed was very tired. He couldn't
stay awake. What a pity Tidyup wouldn't
let him sleep in that big cosy flower.

But he found a nice shady spot and
settled down for another snooze.
He was just drifting off when . . .

. . . Wash-Your-Face passed by!

Oh dear! Perhaps Go-to-Bed should find somewhere more peaceful.

He thought he would be quiet and undisturbed in a gherkin patch.

But not the gherkin patch at the end of Clean-Your-Teeth's garden.

He tried resting at the bottom of a great big rock.

Go-and-Play's rock! Go-to-Bed wasn't
having much luck finding somewhere
to go to sleep. He decided to move on.

He passed Tidyup's place again.
Tidyup was still admiring his
new flower.

Go-to-Bed wished so much he could sleep in there!

Go-to-Bed thought he might find peace and quiet on the dump.

As usual, Stoppit popped out to see
what was going on.

Go-to-Bed settled down by an old tv set, and, as he dozed off . . .

. . . he switched the tv on! Stoppit thought that was terrific.

So, too, did all the other folk in the land of Do-As-You're-Told.

They came rushing over to the
dump to see the show.

Go-to-Bed wasn't going to get any sleep there either. It seemed he was the only one in the whole land who didn't love television.

Even Tidyup came along to watch.

And that gave Go-to-Bed an idea!
So, while everybody else was glued
to the set, he sneaked quietly away.

And found himself a bed at last.